Homework Helpers English

Ages 5–6

Key Stage 1/Year 1

We're the Homework Helpers!

We've thought up lots of fun activities for you!

So grab your pens and pencils...

...and let's get started!

An imprint of Pearson Education

Harlow, England · London · New York · Reading, Massachusetts · San Francisco
Toronto · Don Mills, Ontario · Sydney · Tokyo · Singapore · Hong Kong · Seoul
Taipei · Cape Town · Madrid · Mexico City · Amsterdam · Munich · Paris · Milan

Series editors:
Stuart Wall & Geoff Black
With thanks to Val Mitchell for additional material and Heather Ancient for editorial development work

These people helped us write the book!

A complete range of **Homework Helpers** is available.

		ENGLISH	MATHS	SCIENCE
Key Stage 1	Ages 5–6 Year 1	✓	✓	Science is not included in the National Tests at Key Stage 1
	Ages 6–7 Year 2	✓	✓	
Key Stage 2	Ages 7–8 Year 3	✓	✓	✓
	Ages 8–9 Year 4	✓	✓	✓
	Ages 9–10 Year 5	✓	✓	✓
	Ages 10–11 Year 6	✓	✓	✓

This tells you about all our other books.

Which ones have you got?

Pearson Education Limited
Edinburgh Gate, Harlow
Essex CM20 2JE, England
and Associated Companies throughout the world

First published 2000

British Library Cataloguing in Publication Data
A catalogue entry for this title is available from the British Library

ISBN 0-582-38140-1

Printed in Great Britain by Henry Ling Ltd, at the Dorset Press, Dorchester, Dorset

This is for grown-ups!

Guidance and advice

Schools are now asked to set regular homework, even for young children. Government guidelines for Year 1 (ages 5–6) suggest 1 hour of homework a week. Children are also encouraged to do at least 10–20 minutes of reading each day.

The Literacy Hour

The daily Literacy Hour was introduced into schools in September 1999. During this session, teachers focus on three broad areas: word, sentence and text. The aim of the Literacy Hour is to develop a child's reading and writing skills.

All the activities in this book are written to complement the Literacy Hour. The emphasis is on short, enjoyable exercises designed to stimulate a child's interest in language. Each activity will take 10–20 minutes, depending on the topic, and the amount of writing and drawing.

Themes and topics

Throughout the book key words have been set in **bold** text – these highlight the themes and content of the activities, and provide a guide to the topics covered.

Encourage your child

Leave your child to do the activity on their own, but be available to answer any questions. Try using phrases like: That's a good idea! How do you think you could do it? What happens if you do it this way? These will encourage your child to think about how they could answer the question for themselves.

If your child is struggling ...

Younger children might need help understanding the question before they try to work out an answer, and children who need help with reading or writing may need you to work with them. If your child is struggling with the writing, ask them to find the answer and then write it in for them. Remember even if your child gets stuck, be sure to tell them they are doing well.

The activities start on the next page! Have you got your pens and pencils ready?

Check the answers together

When they have done all they can, sit down with them and go through the answers together. Check they have not misunderstood any important part of the activity. If they have, try to show them why they are going wrong. Ask them to explain what they have done, right or wrong, so that you can understand how they are thinking.

You will find answers to the activities at the back of this book. You can remove the last page if you think your child might look at the answers before trying an activity. Sometimes there is no set answer because your child has been asked for their own ideas. Check that your child's answer is appropriate and shows they have understood the question.

Be positive!

If you think your child needs more help with a particular topic try to think of some similar but easier examples. You don't have to stick to the questions in the book – ask your own: Did you like that? Can you think of any more examples? Have a conversation about the activity. Be positive, giving praise for making an effort and understanding the question, not just getting the right answers. Your child should enjoy doing the activities and at the same time discover that learning is fun.

More on Spelling

Help your child to keep a list of words that they tend to spell incorrectly. Encourage your child to use these words regularly in their own writing, so as to get into the habit of spelling them correctly. Help your child break down words into separate sounds or syllables ('home-work', 'read-ing'). This makes the spelling and reading of unfamiliar words easier.

Children can test themselves in the following way:

Look at the word
Say the spelling out loud
Cover the word so they can't see it
Write it down
Check that it's spelt correctly

Poems, songs and nursery rhymes can help with a child's spellings because they encourage children to develop an awareness of sound patterns and an understanding of the link between sounds and letters.

Who I am

My name is

____

I look like this

Can you draw your picture in the frame?

My address is

____

____

____

____

Can you write your address on the envelope?

I am ________ years old.

Can you draw some candles on the birthday cake?

Alpha rows

*You need to know the **alphabet** to fill in the gaps.*

Fill in the missing letters.

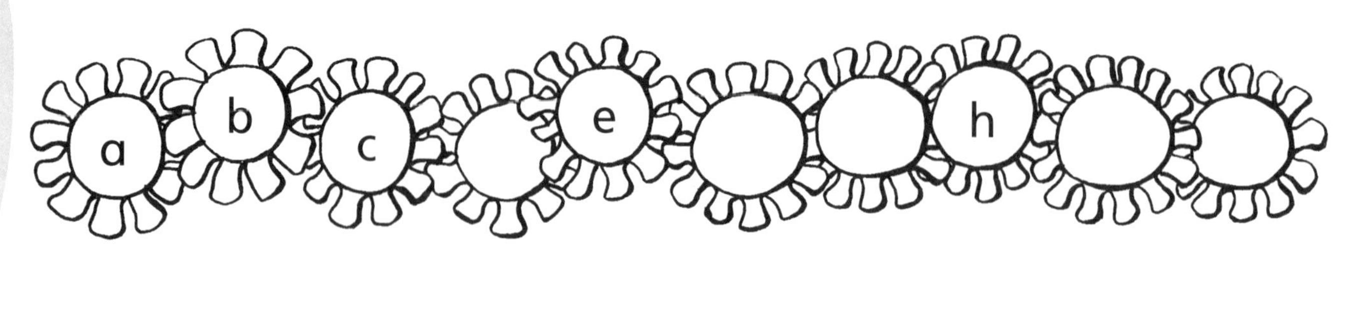

Colour the row that starts with **c** red and yellow.
Colour the row that starts with **q** purple and pink.
Colour the row that ends with **j** orange and black.
Colour the last three flowers green on the row that starts with **h**.

Family search

Can you find these words in the **word puzzle**?

mum dad cat dog girl

brother sister boy people

Put a ring round the words when you find them.

One has been done for you!

b	r	o	t	h	e	r	n	w
p	c	e	g	f	j	k	p	m
e	s	i	s	t	e	r	q	u
o	m	v	w	d	o	g	t	m
p	x	s	t	g	i	r	l	z
l	b	e	v	n	m	q	p	r
e	o	k	l	k	d	a	d	w
j	y	v	c	a	t	x	f	h

To find the words, go across or down.

Days and dates

Read this page from Anna's **diary**.

Monday
I went to the dentist.

Tuesday
I went to the pool for a swim.

Wednesday
I took my PE kit to school.

Thursday
I went on a school trip to the zoo.

Friday
It was Ben's birthday party.

Saturday
I went to the shops on the bus.

Sunday
I played football in the park.

1 Which day did Anna see Ben?

2 Which day did Anna kick a ball?

3 Which day did Anna need her PE kit?

4 Which day did Anna go on a bus?

5 Which day did Anna go for a swim?

6 Which day did the dentist see Anna's teeth?

7 Which day would you like best?

Your diary

Keep your own **diary** for this week.

Picture rhymes

Colour the picture which **rhymes** with the word.

Use a different colour for the wrong answers.

 pen    

2 dish    

3 car    

4 see    

5 dig    

6 log    

Two words rhyme if they end with the same sound, like mouse and house.

Find the word

Put a ring around these words in the **word puzzle**.

they	these	that	them	those
________	________	________	________	________
their	the	than	there	this
________	________	________	________	________

Each time you find a word copy it on the line underneath.

t	h	a	t	d	t	h	e	s	e	t
x	c	t	h	e	m	b	t	l	t	h
v	t	h	a	n	b	l	h	k	h	e
t	m	t	h	o	s	e	e	q	e	y
h	q	p	s	r	u	v	i	w	r	x
e	z	t	h	i	s	a	r	b	e	c

To find the words look across or down.

All the words begin with th.

Match up

Colour each matching pair using a different colour.

Match up the **rhyming words** by following the lines.

Fill the gaps

January February June March

April May

July August September

October November December

These are all ***months*** *of the year.*

Can you complete these words?

Fill in the correct month.

J ___ n ___ a ___ y

F ___ b ___ u ___ r ___

M ___ r ___ h

A ___ r ___ l

M ___ y

J ___ n ___

J u ___ ___

A ___ g ___ s ___

S ___ p ___ e ___ b ___ r

O ___ t ___ b ___ r

N ___ v ___ m ___ e ___

D ___ c ___ m ___ e ___

My birthday is in ____________________

My best friend's birthday is in ____________________

Christmas is in ____________________

The first one has been done for you.

Join the letters to make a **colour word**.

gre	en	own
bl	te	ue
br	d	ange
bla	ck	ow
whi		
re		
yell		
or		

Now write the colours in a list.

____

____

____

____

____

____

____

____

My favourite colour is

____

My hair is ____________________

My eyes are ____________________

orange	red
blue	green
yellow	black
white	brown

Odd word out

Put a ring around the word which **doesn't rhyme**.

1	red	bed	said	good
2	too	blue	three	zoo
3	may	say	them	play
4	that	this	mat	cat
5	hot	pot	pet	got
6	mug	jug	plug	pig
7	wet	sit	pet	let

Get to the middle of the maze and find the word that **rhymes** with rock.

Along the right path are two things which also rhyme with rock. What are they?

Draw a line from the start to the middle.

start

Write down the names of the things which rhyme with rock.

______________ ______________ ______________

Lollipoem

Read this poem out loud.

Lollipop, lollipop,
Red and green,
Lollipop, lollipop,
Best I've seen.
Lollipop, lollipop,
Gone too quick,
Lollipop, lollipop,
Just a stick!

Try making up your own verse. Fill in the missing lines. Can you make them **rhyme**?

Lollipop, lollipop,

Pink and ____________________ ,

Lollipop, lollipop,

____

Lollipop, lollipop,

____________________________ ,

Lollipop, lollipop,

____________________________ .

Make a list of some rhyming words you could use.

You can ask an adult to help you if you get stuck.

What happens next?

Look at the pictures. They tell a story.
Put the right sentence under each picture.

1 ____________________

2 ____________________

3 ____________________

4 ____________________

The cat was stuck in a tree.
The cat was asleep in the garden.
Mum had to get the cat down.
The dog chased the cat.

Where's that cat?

Choose the correct word to show **where** the cat is.

on under between in

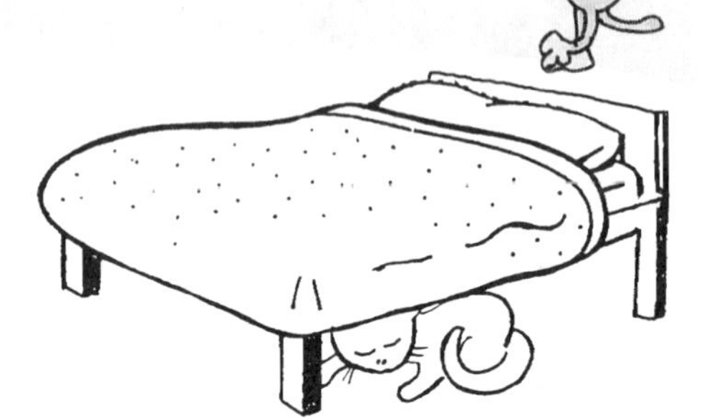

The cat is ________________
the bed.

The cat is ________________
the box.

The cat is ________________
the wall.

The cat is ________________
the dog and the horse.

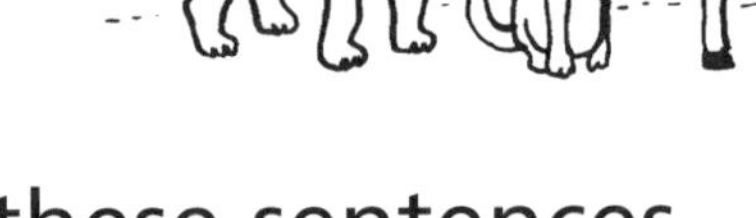

Now draw the pictures for these sentences.

The cat is in the bath.	The cat is up in the tree.

Word families

Can you **match** the **words** to the animals? There are two words to go with each animal.

The first is done for you.

- rabbit
- horse
- goldfish
- budgerigar
- dog
- mouse

gallops	field	barks
birdcage	hops	kennel
hutch	nibbles	bowl
hole	squeaks	swims

Now use each group of three words to make a sentence. You can add extra words of your own.

1 The rabbit nibbles lettuce in his hutch.

2 ______________________________

3 ______________________________

4 ______________________________

5 ______________________________

6 ______________________________

Word puzzle

1 Add ch or sh to make some words:

ch op in eese

sh ip ark urch

Write the words you make here:

__________ __________ __________

__________ __________ __________

__________ __________ __________

2 Use ch or sh at the end to make a word:

lun_____ pu_____ di_____ spla_____

pin_____ mun_____ wi_____ crun_____

Word search

Can you find some words in the word search?
They begin with fl and bl.

The words you should be able to find are:

fly ____________	black ____________
flap ____________	block ____________
flea ____________	blend ____________
flop ____________	blue ____________

When you find a word write it on the line.

You need to look down or across.

f	b	l	e	n	d
l	v	h	z	p	h
y	b	l	a	c	k
f	l	o	p	k	b
p	y	f	e	n	l
b	x	l	o	q	o
l	k	e	v	d	c
u	s	a	k	q	k
e	f	l	a	p	n

Put a ring round the words you find.

The robot twins

Some words **double the last letter** when you add ing or ed. Write the ing and ed words on the lines.

Don't forget you need to double the last letter before you add ed or ing.

Write the ing words on these lines.

One has been done for you.

ing

swim swimming

cut ______

run ______

dig ______

hop ______

sit ______

Write the ed words here.

ed

rub rubbed

tap ______

drop ______

beg ______

fit ______

mop ______

Choose the words from the lists on the opposite page.

Use the double letter 'ing' words to finish these sentences.

1 Mum is ____________________ the grass.

2 Dad is ____________________ the garden.

3 Granny is ____________________ under the tree.

4 The children are ____________________ about.

Use the double letter 'ed' words to finish these sentences.

5 Robbie ________________ his dad to buy him a new bike.

6 Yesterday Mum ________________ the floor.

7 Yesterday the postman ________________ on the door so loudly that Granny ________________ her knitting.

Hot and cold

Draw a line from each picture to one of these sentences.

This place is all ice.

This place has little water.

This place has mountains.

This place has rain and sun.

The North Pole is all ice and snow.
Just a few tiny plants can live there.

Some mountains are very high. Their tops can have snow on all the time.

Lots of animals live in jungles. The hot, wet weather makes many plants grow.

Deserts are places where little rain falls. Most deserts are hot in the day, but not at night.

2 Which place is all white? ____________________

3 Which kind of place is hot and has many animals? ____________________

4 Which places have hot days and cold nights?

____

5 Which kinds of places are high up and can be cold on top? ____________________

1 How many true sentences can you make?

The	North Pole	is	hot
	desert	are	sandy
	mountains		cold
	jungles		high

Choose one thing from each box to make a sentence.

One has been done for you.

The desert is sandy.

____

____

____

2 Which place has camels? ________________

3 Which place has monkeys? ________________

4 Which two places have snow?

________________ and ________________

5 We use these words when we talk about hot and cold places. Sort them into the lists below.

chill frost sunshine freeze

snow ice heat sunny warm

Two words have been done for you.

words for cold places	words for hot places
frost	sunny

Word search

Here are some words for you to find.

train	____________	game	____________
rain	____________	fame	____________
drain	____________	lame	____________
grain	____________	name	____________
brain	____________	same	____________

When you find a word, write it on the line.

Look down and across.

Put a ring round the words you find.

d	r	a	i	n	s	r	a	i	n
w	z	b	m	c	a	s	g	k	r
b	n	r	a	r	m	o	r	r	k
r	a	s	n	n	e	o	a	m	f
a	m	a	g	a	m	e	i	p	a
i	e	l	a	m	e	x	n	q	m
n	h	o	t	r	a	i	n	z	e

Word magic

Change the top word into the bottom word by filling in the answers to the clues below.

You must change only one letter at a time.

Clue	Answer
Faster than walk	run
A sticky cake with currants in it	________
A flower before it blooms	________
Where you sleep at night	bed

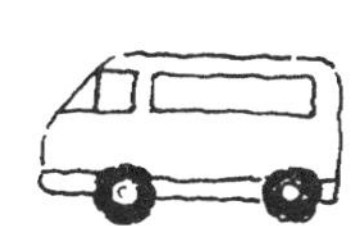

Clue	Answer
A sort of car for carrying goods	van
A grown-up boy	________
Another word for crazy	________
Earth when it is wet and sticky	mud

Ending words

Backpack Jack

Jack put on his backpack,
He needed to be quick.
He ran fast down the track,
To meet his old mate Nick.

Jill climbed up a big hill.
Her boots did not fit well.
She kept on going till
Her feet began to swell.

List all the words that end in ck and ll.

ck	ll

Can you think of any other words that end in ck and ll? Add them to your list.

2 Use the letters in the boxes to finish the words.

use	use	use
g n b t d	g n m d p	g n b t x
bi___	di___	fi___
bi___	di___	fi___
bi___	di___	fi___
bi___	di___	fi___
bi___	di___	fi___

3 What letters can you use to finish these words?

mu___	cu___	ru___
mu___	cu___	ru___
mu___	cu___	ru___

Naughty puppy

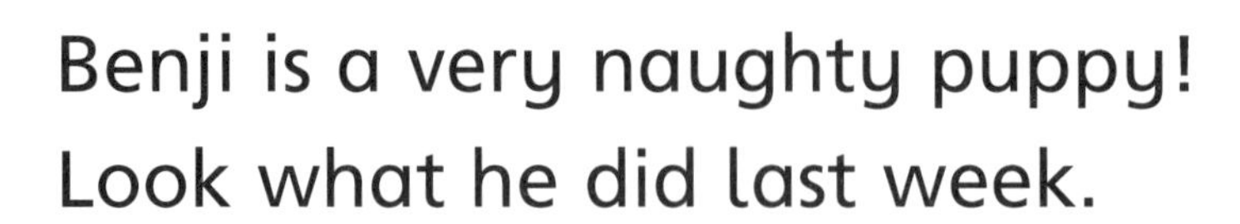

Benji is a very naughty puppy!
Look what he did last week.

Monday

Tuesday

Wednesday

Thursday

Friday

Saturday

Sunday

What did Benji do?

Write a **sentence** for each day.

These words may help you:

Don't forget the ***full stop*** *at the end of the sentence.*

ate the cake

woke the baby

made a puddle on the floor

chewed a slipper

pulled down the curtains

dug a big hole in the garden

chased the cat

On Monday Benji ______

On ______

On ______

On ______

On ______

On ______

On ______

At the vet's

Read these poems about the vet's.

My little fish was ill
so we took her to the vet.
We couldn't take her tank
so I caught her in a net.

I had to dip down deep
for she hid away from us.
I put her in a bowl
and took her on the bus.

I'm here about my dog.
He is getting very fat.
He doesn't like to jog
or even chase the cat.

The vet said, "Feed him less,
he really must get thinner",
so I give him tiny meals –
but he goes next door for dinner!

Now answer these questions.

1 Which pet doesn't like to jog? ______________

2 Which pet came to the vet's by bus?

____

3 Where does the dog go to get more food?

____

4 Write out the words the vet says:

____

5 What letter do these words begin with?

___og ___ish ___et ___owl

___us ___ank ___oor ___inner

Change the top word into the bottom word by finding the answers to the clues.

You must only change one letter at a time.

Clue		Answer
A fast sort of aeroplane		jet
An animal you own		______
Something you write with		______
It is sharp and holds things together		pin

Clue		Answer
It has a pastry top and a filling		pie
An apple tree grows from this		______
This is on the outside of your mouth		______
The top part of your legs when you are sitting down		lap

Here are some more words for you to find.

They all have ee or ea in the middle of them.

feet	________	meat	________
meet	________	seat	________
week	________	beat	________
leek	________	leak	________
been	________	beak	________

When you find a word, write it on the line.

b	e	e	n	p	b	e	a	t
m	f	w	m	e	e	t	b	l
e	e	w	e	e	k	f	s	e
a	l	x	p	u	b	e	b	e
t	g	l	e	a	k	e	e	k
q	b	f	k	b	r	t	a	m
s	e	a	t	e	l	y	k	v

Look down and across to find the words.

PE poem

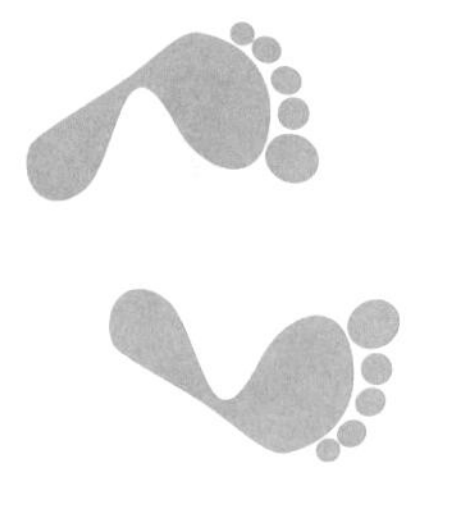

Socks off. Jump!
Shorts on. Hop!
Just keep moving,
till I say "Stop!"

Legs jog,
arms bend.
Don't talk
to your friend!

Along the beam.
Don't fall!
Keep your balance,
walk tall.

Climb the ropes.
Don't be slow,
to the top –
up you go!

Well done!
That's really nice!
Now line up,
quiet as mice.

The verses have four lines each. Two of them rhyme.

Read the poem out loud. Ask someone to listen to you. Try to sound like a PE teacher giving orders. Use a loud voice!

1 How many **verses** are there in the poem?

____

2 Which two words in each verse **rhyme**?

________________ and ________________

________________ and ________________

________________ and ________________

________________ and ________________

________________ and ________________

3 How does the PE lesson end? ________________

____

____

Moles

Moles live in homes underground. Here they are well hidden from their enemies – cats, stoats and weasels. Moles dig long tunnels. They catch insects, larvae and earthworms. They keep the earthworms in special side tunnels which are called larders. They push the soil from their tunnels up to the surface. These form the mole hills that you might see on your lawns.

If you don't know what some of the words mean ask an adult to tell you.

1 Where do moles live?

___

2 Which animals might eat moles?

___

3 What do moles eat?

___

4 Where do moles sometimes keep earthworms?

___

Holiday writing

My Holiday by Jane Vincent

I visited Great-aunt Emma. I went with Granny and Grandpa. We travelled there by train. I took my overnight things with me. When I got there, Great-aunt Emma was practising football! The best part was playing football in the park with Granny, Grandpa and Great-aunt Emma. The worst part was leaving to come home.

Use the **writing frame** to write about *your* holiday.

My Holiday by ______________________

I visited ______________________

I went with ______________________

I travelled there by ______________________

I took ______________________ with me.

When I got there ______________________

____

The best part was ______________________

The worst part was ______________________

Opposites

One has been done for you.

Join the **opposites** with a line.

Now write down the pairs of opposites in the spaces.

__________________ and __________________

__________________ and __________________

__________________ and __________________

__________________ and __________________

__________________ and __________________

__________________ and __________________

Middle sounds

Put in the **middle letters** for each word.

Each time, choose one of the letters from the box.

Changing the middle letter makes a new word.

a e i o u

p ___ t

p ___ t

p ___ t

p ___ t

p ___ t

*a e i o and u are called **vowels**.*

a e i o u

f ___ n

f ___ n

f ___ n

f ___ n

a e i o u

n ___ t

n ___ t

n ___ t

n ___ t

a e i o u

l ___ g

l ___ g

l ___ g

l ___ g

Stop it

Put in the **full stops** and circle letters which should be **capital letters**.

Full stops come at the end of a sentence.

1 i have to go to school on monday i have been on holiday

In each of these, you should make two sentences.

2 i went to school and saw my friends my friends are called sam and raj

3 my teacher's name is miss brown she is new she has a lovely smile

In each of these, you should make three sentences.

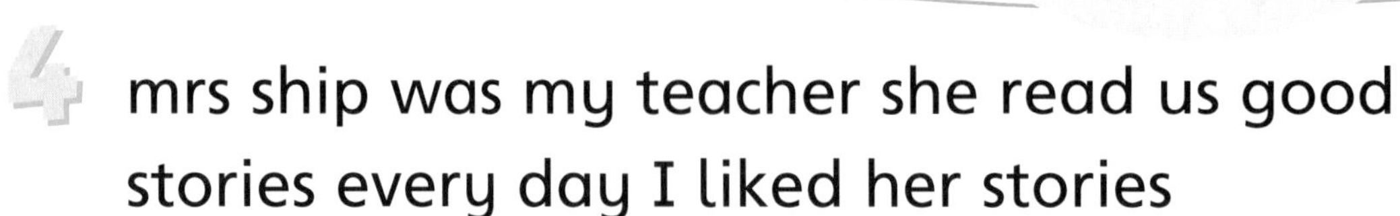

4 mrs ship was my teacher she read us good stories every day I liked her stories

Question mark?

A **question mark** is used to show that you have asked a question.

Can you answer the questions?

1 What is your name?

2 Where do you live?

3 When did you go to bed last night?

4 Who is your teacher?

5 Which is your favourite animal?

6 Make up a question of your own. Write it here and remember the question mark!

Letter change

For each of these, add one of the letters from the box to make a different word.

b c d f g h j k l m n
p q r s t v w x y z

All of these letters are called ***consonants.***

___et ___at ___og

___et ___at ___og

___et ___at ___og

___et ___at ___og

For these, the extra letter goes at the beginning.

For these, the extra letter goes at the end.

ma___ bi___ sa___

ma___ bi___ sa___

ma___ bi___ sa___

ma___ bi___ sa___

Get it right!

Choose the right word to finish each sentence.

1 The flowers had a lovely __________ .

shell
smell

2 The __________ began to ring.

phone
bone

3 The bird put its head under its __________ .

wind
wing

Do you know which is the right word to use?

4 My mum learnt how to __________ a car.

drill
drive

5 Sally went to the bathroom to __________ her hair.

wash
wish

6 Dad will __________ me a birthday cake.

break
bake

Kick off

I love football so Grandad took me to see our team play.

There were lots of steps to climb. Grandad had to go slowly. He got out of breath. It made him gasp and he kept stopping for a rest. Still, we got there in the end, in seats high up in the stand.

Grandad sat down. He pulled on his cap and took off his gloves. Then he twisted the top off his flask of coffee and had a drink.

It was a night match. Everything looked bright in the floodlights. The pitch was so green. It was damp and shiny, as if it were made of glass. The crowd sang lots of songs. "Wish for a win," said Grandad. "Pray for goals. We must be the best tonight."

Then a yell went up. A loud cheer from the crowd. The players were on the pitch.
Then a hush.
A whistle.
Kick off.

Fill in the missing words.

1. I love ____________ .

2. Grandad said, "Pray for ____________ ."

3. Grandad had a flask of ____________ .

4. The pitch looked bright green because of the flood ____________ .

5. Our seat was high up in the ____________ .

6. What did we have to climb? ____________

7. Who sang lots of songs? ____________

8. Look at the **full stops** and **commas** in the story.
These tell you when to pause.
Go over them with coloured crayons. Use one colour for full stops and another for commas.

Witch spell

Wanda the Witch has a spell she thinks will bring her gold and make her rich. Can you fill in her spell so she knows what to drop in her pot?

Choose one of these words to fill in the rhymes.

Gran sink stuff rust

A gust of wind,
A huff and a puff,
A spoon of dust.
Oh, lots of _____ .

A crack from a glass,
A frog and ham flan,
A petal and stem,
A vest from my _____ .

An elf in a mask,
A crumb from a crust,
A fang and a tusk,
A drum full of _____ .

A twig from a stick,
The froth from a drink,
A slug that was quick,
The plug from the _____ .

But Wanda the Witch has no luck. She gets no gold. She is not rich. All she gets is a bag of crisps!

2 Pair up the words with the same **first sounds**.

crop brass slim grill crack
drill drop grass brim slack

crop ________ and crack ________

________ and ________

________ and ________

________ and ________

________ and ________

One has been done for you.

3 Now pair up the words so they **rhyme**.

crop ________ and drop ________

________ and ________

________ and ________

________ and ________

________ and ________

Colour crossword

The answers to the clues in the **crossword** are all colours.

1							
2							
					3		
4			5				6
		7					
			8				

Across

2. This is the colour of a tomato. (3 letters)
4. Half-way between white and black. (4 letters)
7. The colour of the sky on a nice day. (4 letters)
8. The colour of snow. (5 letters)

Down

1. This colour is also the name of a fruit. (6 letters)
3. Many plants are this colour. (5 letters)
5. Change one letter in the word *fellow* to find this colour. (6 letters)
6. If you mix blue and red you get this colour. (6 letters)

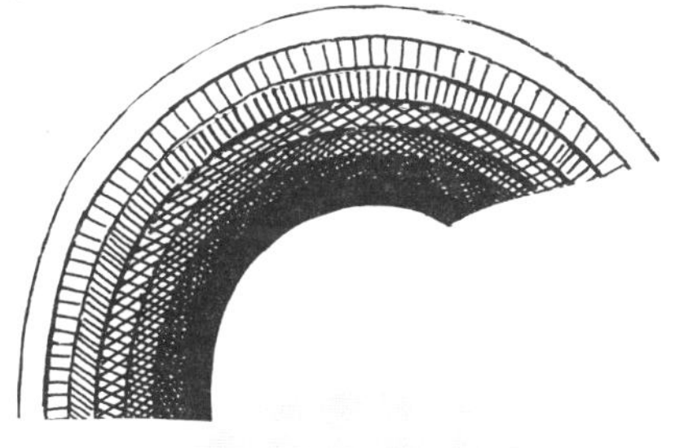

Choose from these colours.

grey orange
red yellow
green blue white
purple

Number search

Can you find these words in the word search?

eight eleven five four nine one
seven six ten three twelve two

To find the words, look across or down.

Start at one and go to twelve.

t	w	e	l	v	e	k
m	e	i	g	h	t	f
s	z	d	t	w	o	o
e	l	e	v	e	n	u
s	e	v	e	n	o	r
f	t	c	s	i	x	x
i	e	o	m	d	q	p
v	n	n	n	i	n	e
e	z	e	l	s	e	v
g	t	h	r	e	e	w

Ring each word when you find it.

Now write the number words below in the correct order.

one ________ ________ ________

________ ________ ________

________ ________ ________

________ ________ ________

Alphabet dot-to-dot

Join the dots in **alphabetical order** – starting of course with the letter a.

Verb webs

Look at the things inside the shape. Think what they might do. These words are 'doing' words.

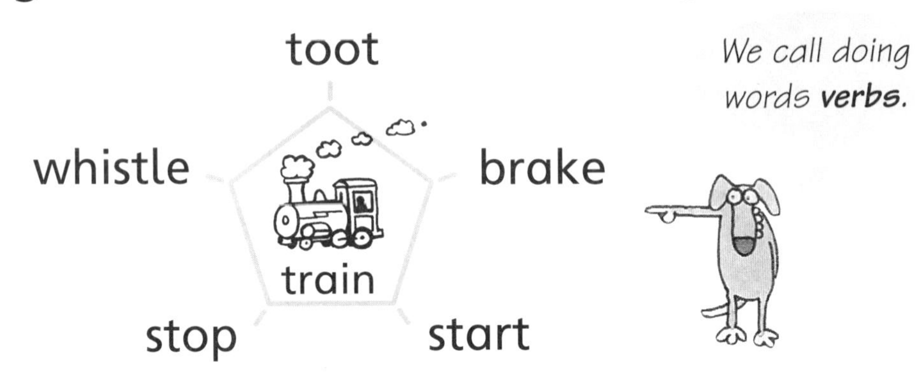

Choose the words from the box at the bottom of the page to fill in the spaces.

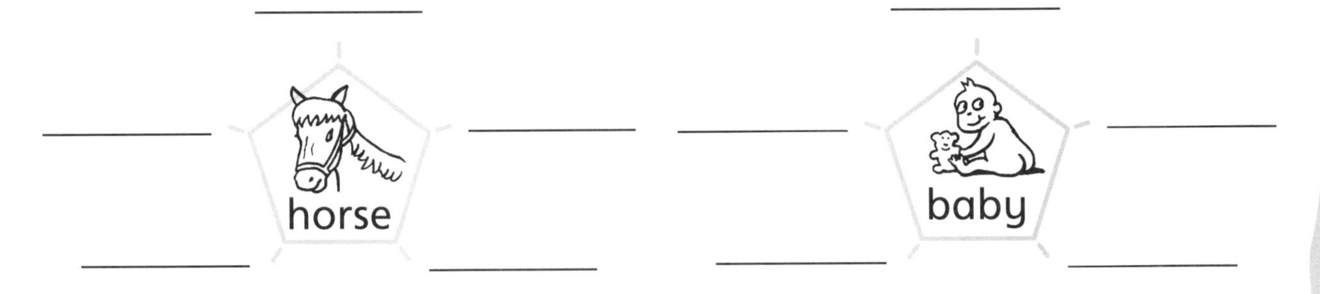

crackle trot laugh cry gallop burn smoke spark neigh canter dribble smile

Write it down

There are lots of ways of **writing**.

A

SALE

LOTS OF BARGAINS

LAST FEW DAYS

B

Dear Tooth Fairy,
I swallowed my tooth at school today, so I couldn't leave it under my pillow.
Mum said you would understand.
Love Victoria

C

potatoes	carrots
butter	bread
apples	bananas
cereal	milk
cheese	

D

Dad,
Dinner in oven!
Mum

E

BEWARE OF THE DOG

1 Which of these is written in capital letters?

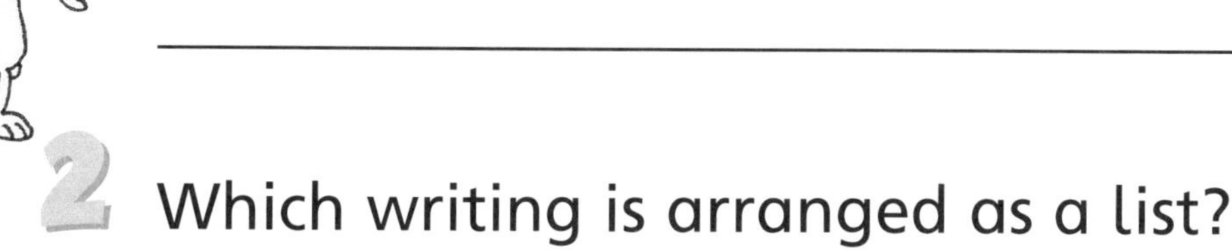

____

2 Which writing is arranged as a list? __________

3 Who is the letter written to? __________

4 Which of these would be handwritten? __________

5 Who is the note about the dinner for? __________

Lost

A Special Teddy Bear

On Monday 9th January between
Holbrook Road and Peak Primary School.

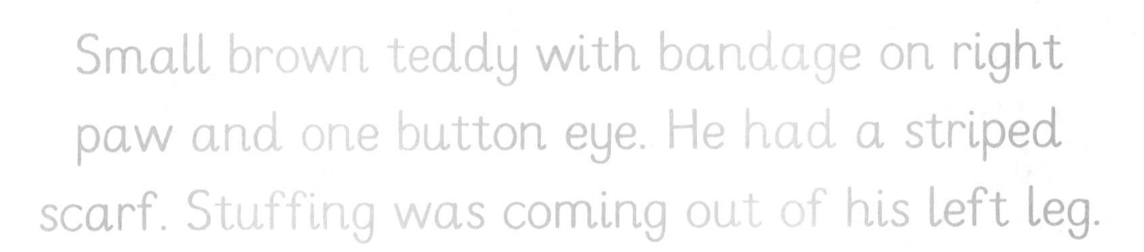

Small brown teddy with bandage on right paw and one button eye. He had a striped scarf. Stuffing was coming out of his left leg.

If you find him please ring
Peak View 01256 98796

PS Please look after him until we can pick him up, as he is my brother's and he misses him.

James's little brother lost his teddy. James **made a poster** to help him find it. His mother put the poster in the newsagent's window.

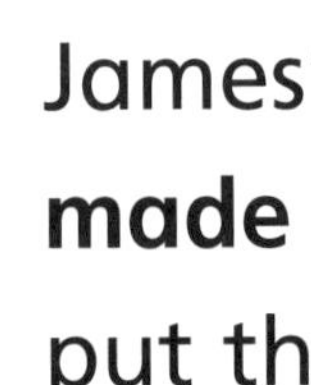

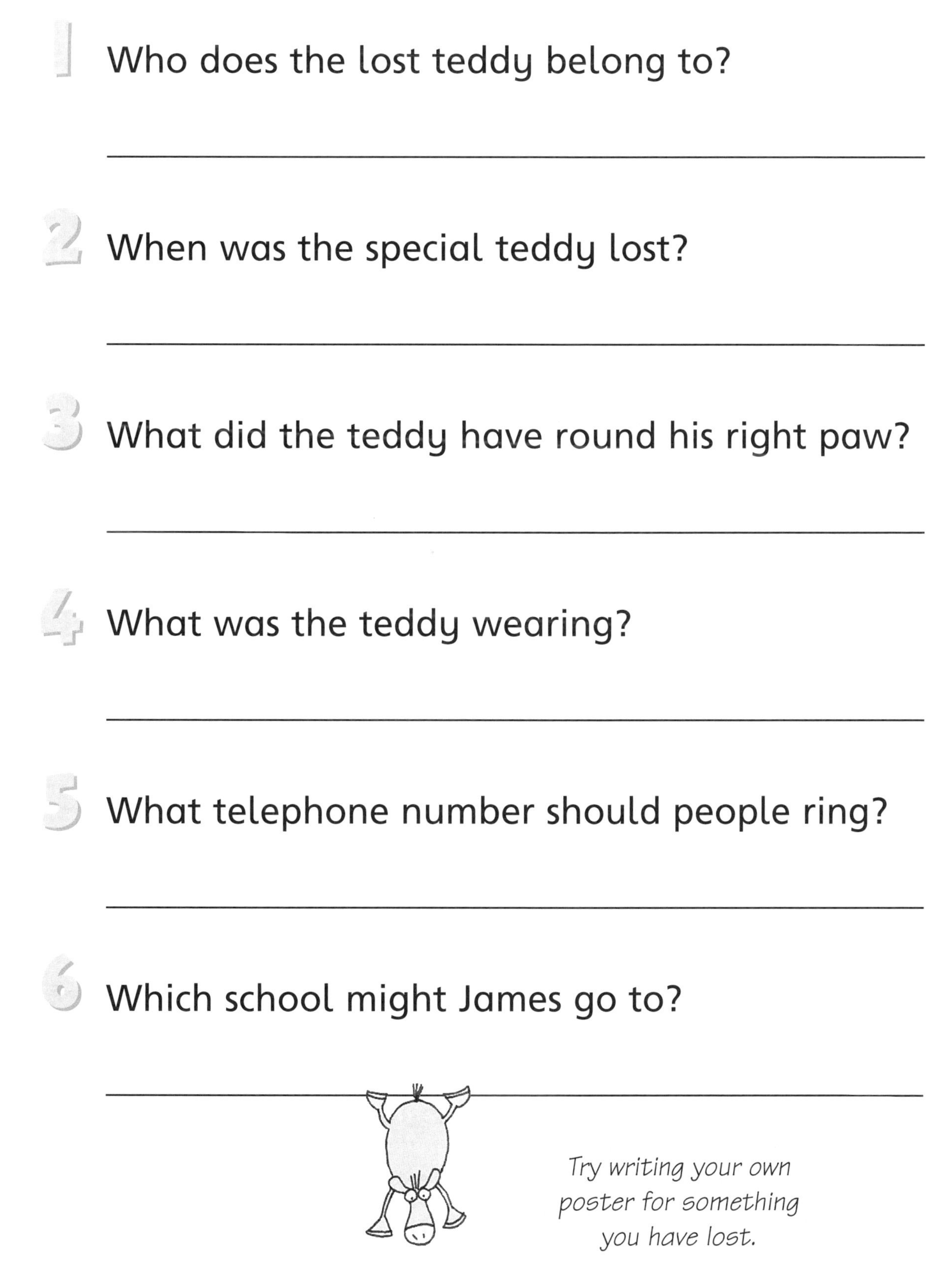

1 Who does the lost teddy belong to?

___

2 When was the special teddy lost?

___

3 What did the teddy have round his right paw?

___

4 What was the teddy wearing?

___

5 What telephone number should people ring?

___

6 Which school might James go to?

___

Try writing your own poster for something you have lost.

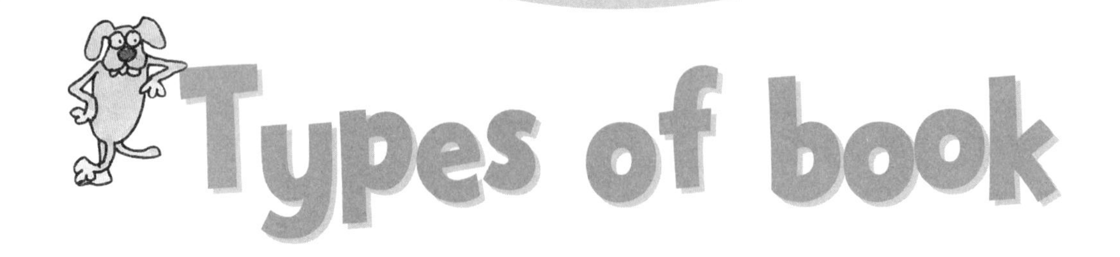

Types of book

Choose a **book** from the library or your bookcase.

Choose the right words to describe your book.

My book is non-fiction / fiction.

It is a hardback / paperback.

Put a ring around the right word.

It has illustrations only / illustrations and text / text only.

The author's name is

____

The title of my book is

____

It looks interesting / uninteresting.

Answers and Hints

Depending on your child's reading ability, you will probably need to help them read some of the texts, or perhaps even read the texts to your child. In activities that require creativity on your child's part, they may need help to get started. You might find it useful to spend a few minutes discussing how they might go about tackling the task. At school the teacher would make sure that the class or group generated some examples and ideas before beginning to complete the work by themselves.

In some instances there may be more than one possible answer so you may need to check that the answer your child has given is reasonable. As long as your child's answer makes sense and has shown they understand the question, you should mark it right. Sometimes the question will ask them to fill in facts about themselves, or to express an opinion, or to create their own piece of work. You may want to judge your child's effort for yourself, but please remember that encouragement is always more helpful than criticism.

PAGE 5
This activity gives your child the opportunity to answer some simple questions about themselves.

PAGE 6
missing letters (and colouring): (first row) d, f, g, i, j – coloured orange and black; (second row) j, k, n, o, p – last three flowers coloured green; (third row) t, u, w, x, z – coloured purple and pink; (fourth row) e, g, j, k – coloured red and yellow

PAGE 7

b	r	o	t	h	e	r	n	w
p	c	e	g	f	j	k	p	m
e	s	i	s	t	e	r	q	u
o	m	v	w	d	o	g	t	m
p	x	s	t	g	i	r	l	z
l	b	e	v	n	m	q	p	r
e	o	k	l	k	d	a	d	w
j	y	v	c	a	t	x	f	h

PAGES 8 & 9
1 Friday 2 Sunday 3 Wednesday 4 Saturday 5 Tuesday 6 Monday 7 Your child should make their own choice here.

PAGE 10
Many children enjoy keeping diaries and the regular writing practice helps to develop writing skills. Your child may want to draw pictures of what happens to them as well.

PAGE 11
1 (coloured picture) hen 2 fish 3 star 4 bee 5 pig 6 dog

PAGE 12
Check that your child has copied the words correctly.

t	h	a	t	d	t	h	e	s	e	t
x	c	t	h	e	m	b	t	l	t	h
v	t	h	a	n	b	l	h	k	h	a
t	m	t	h	o	s	e	e	q	e	t
h	q	p	s	r	u	v	i	w	r	u
e	z	t	h	i	s	a	r	b	e	n

PAGE 13
rhyming pairs (each pair coloured the same): day–play, bed–red, green–seen, men–ten, three–she

PAGE 14
completed words: January, February, March, April, May, June, July, August, September, October, November, December
This task will give your child some practice in spelling the names of the months. Check that you child has written the correct month for their birthday, and for their best friend's birthday (Christmas, of course, is in December).

PAGE 15
colours (top to bottom): green, blue, brown, black, white, red, yellow, orange. This task will give your child some practice in spelling colours. Check that your child has written in their favourite colour correctly, along with the colours of their hair and eyes.

PAGE 16
1 (circled word) good 2 three 3 them 4 this 5 pet 6 pig 7 sit

PAGE 17
words that rhyme with rock (any order): flock, clock, sock

PAGE 18
Check your child has thought of rhyming words to complete the poem. You may need to sit down with your child while they are working on this activity and talk about what words they could use.

PAGE 19
1 The cat was asleep in the garden. 2 The dog chased the cat. 3 The cat was stuck in a tree. 4 Mum had to get the cat down.

PAGE 20
missing words (in order): under, in, on, between Check your child's drawings of the cat in the bath and up in the tree.

PAGE 21
You child may have written slightly different sentences from the ones given here. Mark them correct provided the sentences are sensible and use all the words. 2 the horse gallops in the field 3 the goldfish swims in the bowl 4 the budgerigar hops in the birdcage 5 the dog barks in the kennel 6 the mouse squeaks in the hole Check that your child's sentences are accurate

PAGE 22
1 (completed words, any order) chop, shop, chin, shin, cheese, chip, ship, shark, church (there are nine possible words in total) 2 (completed words, first row) lunch, push, dish, splash; (second row) pinch, munch, wish, crunch

PAGE 23
Check that your child has copied the words correctly.

f	b	l	e	n	d
l	v	h	z	p	h
y	b	l	a	c	k
f	l	o	p	k	b
p	y	f	e	n	l
b	x	l	o	q	o
l	k	e	v	d	c
u	s	a	k	q	k
e	f	l	a	p	n

PAGES 24 & 25
missing words: ('ing' words) cutting, running, digging, hopping, sitting; ('ed' words) tapped, dropped, begged, fitted, mopped
1 (missing word) cutting 2 digging 3 sitting 4 running 5 begged 6 mopped 7 tapped, dropped

PAGES 26 & 27
1 Check that your child has connected the pictures and the statements correctly. 2 North Pole 3 jungle 4 deserts 5 mountains

PAGES 28 & 29
1 (there are three possible sentences) The jungles are hot. The mountains are high. The North Pole is cold. 2 desert 3 jungle 4 North Pole, mountains 5 (words for cold places, any order) chill, snow, ice, freeze; (words for hot places) sunshine, heat, warm

PAGE 30
Check that your child has copied the words correctly.

d	r	a	i	n	s	r	a	i	n
w	z	b	m	c	a	s	g	k	r
b	n	r	a	r	m	o	r	r	k
r	a	s	n	n	e	o	a	m	f
a	m	a	g	a	m	e	i	p	a
i	e	l	a	m	e	x	n	q	m
n	h	o	t	r	a	i	n	z	e

PAGE 31
(missing words, first task) bun, bud; (second task) man, mad

PAGES 32 & 33
1 (words that end in ck) Jack, backpack, quick, track, Nick; (words that end in ll) Jill, hill, well, till, swell (also check any other words that your child has added to these lists) 2 (completed words) big, bin, bib, bit, bid; dig, din, dim, did, dip; fig, fin, fib, fit, fix
3 (any three words from each of these lists) mud, mug, mum; cub, cud, cup, cut; rub, rug, rum, run, rut

PAGES 34 & 35
Encourage your child to write in complete sentences. If they have finished the sentences using their own words check that they have done so sensibly (possible answers (using the words given): On Monday Benji chased the cat. On Tuesday Benji made a puddle on the floor. On Wednesday Benji chewed a slipper. On Thursday Benji ate the cake. On Friday Benji dug a big hole in the garden. On Saturday Benji woke the baby. On Sunday Benji pulled down the curtains.)

PAGES 36 & 37
1 dog 2 fish 3 next door 4 Feed him less, he really must get thinner 5 (completed words, first row) dog, fish, net. bowl; (second row) bus, tank, door, dinner

PAGE 38
missing words: (first task) pet, pen; (second task) pip, lip

PAGE 39
Check that your child has copied the words correctly.

b	e	e	n	p	b	e	a	t
m	f	w	m	e	e	t	b	l
e	e	w	e	e	k	f	s	e
a	l	x	p	u	b	e	b	e
t	g	l	e	a	k	e	e	k
q	b	f	k	b	r	t	a	m
s	e	a	t	e	l	y	k	v

PAGES 40 & 41
1 5 (you may need to discuss with your child what verses are and how to distinguish them) 2 (rhyming pairs, any order) hop–stop, bend–friend, fall–tall, slow–go, nice–mice 3 the children line up/the children are told to line up

PAGE 42
It is always a good idea to encourage your child to write in sentences, although at this age one word answers are acceptable.
1 underground 2 cats, stoats and weasels 3 insects, larvae and earthworms 4 in special side tunnels called larders

PAGE 43
Check that your child has written sensible answers describing their holiday. A writing frame helps your child become familiar with the structure needed in written work. You could talk to them about the need for a beginning, a middle and an end.

PAGE 44
connected opposites: dry–wet, sad–happy, awake–asleep, cold–hot, day–night
Check that your child has copied the words correctly.

PAGE 45
(completed words, top left) pat, pet, pit, pot, put; (top right) fan, fen, fin, fun (check that they haven't written 'fot'); (bottom left) net, nit, not, nut (check that they haven't written 'nat'); (bottom right) lag, leg, log, lug (check that they haven't written 'lig')
Talk to your child about the meaning of any unfamiliar words.

PAGE 46
1 (capital letters should have been circled) I have to go to school on Monday. I have been on holiday. 2 I went to school and saw my friends. My friends are called Sam and Raj. 3 My teacher's name is Miss Brown. She is new. She has a lovely smile.
4 Mrs Ship was my teacher. She read us good stories every day. I liked her stories.

PAGE 47
Check that your child has answers the questions about themselves correctly, and has used the question mark correctly in their own question.

PAGE 48
There are many possible answers – but make sure that whatever words your child makes are real ones! (possible answers: (first column) get, jet, let, met, net, pet, set, vet, wet, yet; (second column) cat, fat, hat, mat, pat, rat, sat, vat; (third column) cog, dog, fog, hog, jog, log; (fourth column) mad, man, map, mar, mat, may; (fifth column) bid, big, bin, bit; (sixth column) sad, sag, sap, sat, saw, say)

PAGE 49
1 (missing word) smell 2 phone 3 wing 4 drive 5 wash
6 bake

PAGES 50 & 51
1 (missing word) football 2 goals 3 coffee 4 lights 5 stand
6 lots of steps 7 the crowd 8 Check that your child has correctly coloured the full stops and commas using different colours.

PAGES 52 & 53
1 (missing words, in order) stuff, Gran, rust, sink 2 (words pairs, same first sounds) brass–brim, slim–slack, grill–grass, drill–drop
3 (words pairs, rhyming) brass–grass, slim–brim, grill–drill, crack–slack

PAGES 54 & 55
across: (2) red, (4) grey, (7) blue, (8) white
down: (1) orange, (3) green, (5) yellow, (6) purple

PAGE 56

t	w	e	l	v	e	k
m	e	i	g	h	t	f
s	z	d	t	w	o	o
e	l	e	v	e	n	u
s	e	v	e	n	o	r
f	t	c	s	i	x	x
i	e	o	m	d	p	q
v	n	n	n	i	n	e
e	z	e	l	s	e	v
g	t	h	r	e	e	w

Check that you child has written out the numbers from one to twelve in the correct order below the grid.

PAGE 57
The picture is of a sheriff's badge; check that your child has joined in the letters in the correct sequence.

PAGE 58
missing verbs: (fire) crackle, burn, smoke, spark; (horse) trot, gallop, neigh, canter; (baby) laugh, cry, dribble, smile

PAGE 59
1 A & E 2 C 3 B 4 B, C & D 5 Dad

PAGES 60 & 61
1 James's little brother 2 Monday 9th January 3 a bandage
4 a striped scarf 5 01256 98796 6 Peak Primary School

PAGE 62
You might need to discuss some of the terms used to describe a book with your child.